D1667106

DO CANDIES SPEAK?

By DOLORES D. BENNETT

Illustrated by SOCRATES BARTOLO

Edited by KARA SCHILLER

The students had just left the classroom and Ms. Carla was writing something on the board for the next day when a voice piped up behind her, "Ms. Carla, do candies speak?"

Ms. Carla turned around and saw Little D. "Hi Little D, what was your question?" she asked.

"Well, I'm not really sure..." Little D confessed, "but I want to know something: do candies speak?"

Bulletin Board

Ms. Carla smiled at Little D and teased lightly, "Well, did they speak to you?"

"Kinda... I heard something. It was loud and clear, but it wasn't through my ears; it was inside me," Little D explained.

Ms. Carla realized that Little D was serious and invited her to sit down. Smiling, she said, "Ok, Little D, tell me about these talking candies."

Little D sat straight up in her chair and began, "Yesterday, my brother and I went to a birthday party. We were the first ones to arrive, and I went straight to the party room while my brother went to the restroom."

"In the party room, I saw all kinds of candies on the table. I took a couple and ate them while deciding where to sit down," Little D said and then stopped.

"And then what happened?" Ms. Carla asked.

"As soon as I sat down, I decided to go back
to the candy table and fill my pockets with
candies. So I did. Then I went back
to my seat and ate some more," she said,
and stopped again.

"And then?" Ms. Carla asked gently.

"The candies were so good, I decided to fill my bag up with candies. But when I got there, I saw my brother scoop out and pocket even more candies than I had! *'He got a lot! That was wrong!'* I thought. But then I heard something inside me say: *'That is exactly what you did!'*" Little D explained.

"What made you think it was the candies that spoke to you?" asked Ms. Carla.

"Because there was no one there but my brother and me. Besides, I would've heard it differently if it was a person…" Little D tried to find the right words, "I heard this voice inside of me."

"Did you talk back to the candies?" Ms Carla asked, smiling.

Little D shook her head and said seriously, "The voice made me feel bad for what I did, so I gave away all the candies away when I got home."

"I believe I know what you're talking about, Little D, and it's not the candies," Ms. Carla said reassuringly, "it's your conscience." Ms. Carla got up and wrote the word on the board.

"What is con-shens?" asked Little D.

"Your conscience is your sense of right and wrong," she explained. "You don't hear it with your ears, but you sense what it's telling you. It let you know that you were wrong to take so many candies. That caused you to give them away instead of keeping them all for yourself."

"So, it's not the candies that spoke?" Little D asked.

"No, Little D, candies don't speak," assured Ms. Carla.

As they walked out of the classroom Little D asked a question: "Is it good to have a conscience, Ms. Carla?"

"Of course it is!" Ms. Carla laughed, "If you didn't have conscience, you might have eaten all those candies and made yourself sick."

"Then I'm glad I have a conscience!" Little D said happily.

"... we are confident that we have a good conscience in all things desiring to live honorably."

Hebrews 13:18